Edexcel GCSE (9–1)
Combined Science
Lab Book 1

C000008237

Contents

Published by Pearson Education Limited, 80 Strand, London, WC2R 0RL.

Text © Mark Levesley, Penny Johnson, Sue Kearsey,
Iain Brand, Nigel Saunders

Series editor: Mark Levesley

Typeset & illustrated by Tech-Set Ltd, Gateshead

Original illustrations © Pearson Education Limited

Cover design by Peter Stratton

The rights of Mark Levesley, Penny Johnson, Sue Kearsey, Iain Brand, Nigel Saunders, Sue Robilliard to be identified as authors of this work have been asserted by them in accordance with the Copyright, Designs and Patents Act 1988.

The Publishers would like to thank Allison Court and John Kavanagh for their contributions to the text.

First published 2016

© Pearson Education Ltd 2016. This material is not copyright free.

Cover image: Science Photo Library Ltd: NASA

All other media © Pearson Education

Pearson Education Limited is not responsible for the content of any external internet sites. It is essential for tutors to preview each website before using it in class so as to ensure that the URL is still accurate, relevant and appropriate. We suggest that tutors bookmark useful websites and consider enabling students to access them through the school/college intranet.

A note from the Publishers: Pearson Education Limited: This resource is based on the March 2016 accredited version of the specification. The worksheets and tests in this resource have not been reviewed or endorsed by Edexcel and should not be considered as being published by Edexcel.

Copies of official specifications for all Edexcel qualifications may be found on the website: www.edexcel.com

While the Publishers have made every attempt to ensure that advice on the qualification and its assessment is accurate, the official specification and associated assessment guidance materials are the only authoritative source of information and should always be referred to for definitive guidance. Pearson examiners have not contributed to any sections in this resource relevant to examination papers for which they have responsibility. Examiners will not use this resource as a source of material for any assessment set by Pearson.

The worksheets and tests are not required to achieve this Pearson qualification. It is not the only suitable material available to support the qualification, and any resource lists produced by the awarding body shall include appropriate resources.

 Pearson

- light microscope

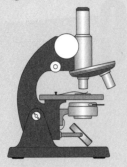

- transparent ruler

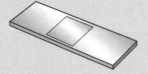

- microscope slide and coverslip

- pipette

- gloves

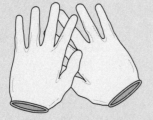

- wooden toothpick/cocktail stick

- sterile wooden spatula/tongue depressor

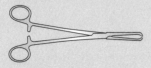

- forceps

- iodine solution in dropping bottle

- dimple tile

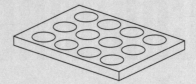

- test tubes

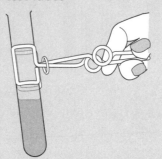

- syringes

- stop clock

- two-holed bung with delivery tube in one hole connected to rubber tubing

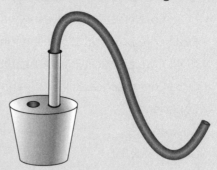

- trough containing water

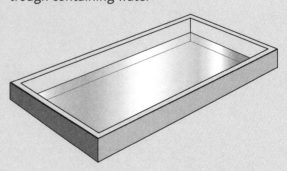

- 100 cm³ conical flask

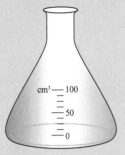

- measuring cylinder

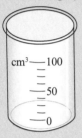

- clamp stand and boss

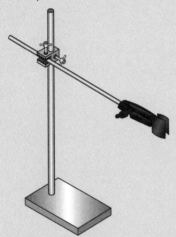

- eye protection

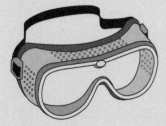

- test tube rack

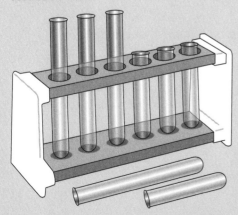

- conical flask with side arm

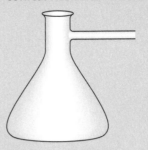

- delivery tube

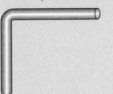

- Bunsen burner

- gauze

- rubber bung with thermometer

- beaker

- tripod

- heat-resistant mat

- Petri dish or watch glass

- evaporating basin

- spatula

- stirring rod

- filter funnel

- filter paper

- tongs

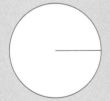

- water bath (set at 50 °C)

- ±0.1 g balance

- white tile

- trolley

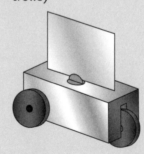

- ramp

- blocks to prop up the end of the ramp

- string

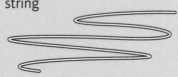

Combined science

- pulley

- masses

- datalogger

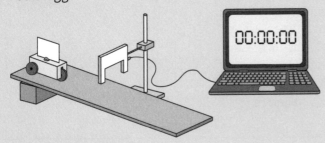

- light gate

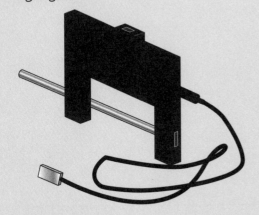

- ripple tank

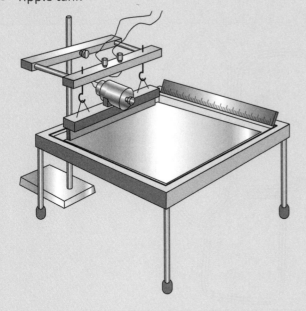

- metre rule

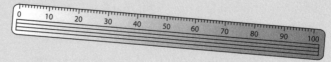

- hammer

- long metal rod

- rubber bands

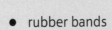

- ray box with single slit

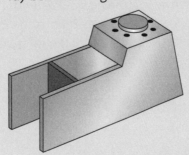

- power supply

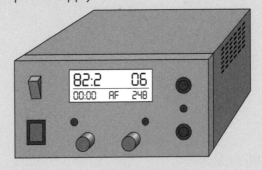

- rectangular glass block

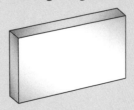

- protractor

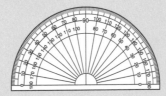

Examining specimens using a microscope and then making labelled drawings of them is a basic skill that you will need in your study of biology. This practical gives you an opportunity to practise this skill.

Your teacher may watch to see if you can:

- handle microscopes and slides carefully and safely.

Method 1: Examining pre-prepared slides of cells

A   You will be changing the magnification of your microscope during this section of the practical. Use the box below to record all of your calculations. Set up your microscope on the lowest magnification objective lens. Work out the total magnification and measure the diameter of the field of view (by using the microscope to observe a transparent ruler).

B   Put the next most powerful objective lens in place. Work out the magnification and by how much it has increased from the magnification in step **A** (e.g. moving from a ×10 to a ×50 is an increase of 5 times). Now divide the diameter of the field of view from step A by the increase in magnification to give you the new diameter of the field of view (e.g. if the field of view in step **A** was 2 mm, then 2 ÷ 5 = 0.4 mm). Do this for each objective lens. Record the total magnification and field of view diameter for each objective lens.

C   Now go back to the lowest magnification objective lens and observe a prepared slide.

D   Use higher magnifications to observe the cells. Estimate the sizes using your field of view diameters.

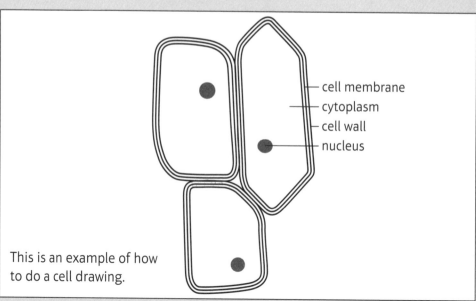

- cell membrane
- cytoplasm
- cell wall
- nucleus

This is an example of how to do a cell drawing.

E Using a sharp pencil, draw 4–5 cells in the box below. There is an example of how to do a microscope drawing in the box on the previous page. Identify and label the cells' parts. Use a ruler to draw your label lines. Write on the magnification. Add any sizes that you have estimated. Have a look for mitochondria (you may not find any as they are very difficult to see).

Method 2: Examining your cheek cells

A   Using the pipette, add a small drop of water to the slide.

B   Stroke the inside of your cheek gently with the wooden spatula. You only want to collect loose cells, so do not scratch the inside of your mouth.

C   Use the end of the spatula that has been in your mouth to stir the drop of water on the slide. Place the used spatula in disinfectant.

D   Put on gloves and use a pipette to add a small drop of methylene blue stain. This makes cells easier to see.

E   Place a coverslip onto the slide at a 45° angle on one edge of the drop. Then use a toothpick to gently lower the coverslip down onto the drop, as shown in the diagram.

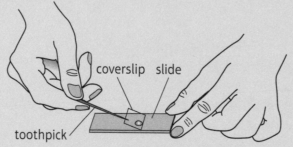

coverslip   slide

toothpick

Avoid trapping air bubbles, which appear as black-edged circles under a microscope.

F   Touch a piece of paper towel to any liquid that spreads out from under the coverslip.

G   Use the lowest magnification objective lens to observe the slide. The nuclei of the cheek cells will be dark blue.

H   Use higher magnifications to observe the cells. Estimate the sizes using your field of view diameters.

I   Using a sharp pencil, draw 4–5 cells in the box below. Identify and label the cells' parts. Use a ruler to draw your label lines. Write on the magnification. Add any sizes that you have estimated. Have a look for mitochondria (you may not find any as they are very difficult to see).

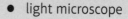

Apparatus

- light microscope
- lamp
- microscope slide
- coverslip
- methylene blue stain
- pipette
- paper towel
- water
- gloves
- wooden toothpick/ cocktail stick
- sterile wooden spatula/ tongue depressor
- disinfectant

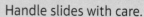

Safety ⚠

Handle slides with care.

Anything that you have put into your mouth should be placed in disinfectant after use.

Wear gloves if using stains.

Wear eye protection.

Method 3: Examining onion or rhubarb stem cells

A If you are going to look at onion cells, put on gloves and use a pipette to add a drop of iodine solution to a microscope slide. If you are going to look at rhubarb, add a drop of water to a microscope slide.

B Using forceps, remove a very small piece of the thin 'skin' on the inside of the fleshy part of the onion. It is very thin indeed and quite tricky to handle. Or remove a thin piece of red 'skin' from a rhubarb stem.

C Place the small piece of skin on the drop on the slide.

D Place a coverslip onto the slide at a 45° angle on one edge of the drop. Then use a toothpick to gently lower the coverslip down onto the drop, as shown in the diagram. Avoid trapping air bubbles, which appear as black-edged circles under a microscope.

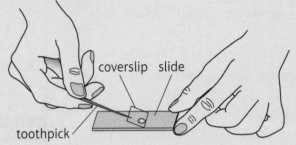
coverslip slide
toothpick

E Touch a piece of paper towel to any liquid that spreads out from under the coverslip.

F Use the lowest magnification objective lens to observe the slide. Then use higher magnifications to observe the cells in more detail. Estimate sizes as you observe.

G Using a sharp pencil, draw 4–5 cells in the box below. Identify the cells' parts and label them. Use a ruler to draw your label lines. Write on the magnification. Add any sizes that you have estimated. Have a look for mitochondria (you may not find any as they are very difficult to see).

Apparatus

- light microscope
- lamp
- microscope slide
- coverslip
- iodine stain
- pipette
- paper towel
- water
- forceps
- wooden toothpick
- piece of onion bulb or rhubarb stem
- gloves

Safety ⚠

Handle slides and microscopes with care.

Wear gloves if using stains.

Wear eye protection.

Method 4: Examining pondweed

A Tear off a very small piece of pondweed leaf: a square with sides of up to 2 mm.

B Place the leaf sample onto a microscope slide and add a drop of water.

C Place a coverslip onto the slide at a 45° angle on one edge of the drop. Then use a toothpick to gently lower the coverslip down onto the drop, as shown in the diagram on page 8. Avoid trapping air bubbles, which appear as black-edged circles under a microscope.

D Touch a piece of paper towel to any liquid that spreads out from under the coverslip.

E Use the lowest magnification objective lens to observe the slide.

F Use higher magnifications to observe the cells in more detail. Estimate sizes as you observe.

G Using a sharp pencil, draw 4–5 cells in the box below. Identify the cells' parts and label them. Use a ruler to draw your label lines. Write on the magnification. Add any sizes that you have estimated. If you watch very carefully when you have the cells under a high magnification, you may well see the chloroplasts moving as the cytoplasm moves inside the cells.

Apparatus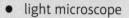

- light microscope
- lamp
- microscope slide
- coverslip
- iodine stain
- pipette
- paper towel
- water
- forceps
- wooden toothpick
- piece of pondweed

Safety ⚠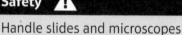

Handle slides and microscopes with care.
Wear eye protection.

Use this section to record what you have learnt in this practical.
I can...

- ☐ identify the parts of plant and animal cells
- ☐ calculate total magnification using a formula
- ☐ make drawings of plant and animal cells using a light microscope and identify their parts
- ☐ estimate sizes using microscope fields of view.

Exam-style questions

1 A microscope is fitted with three objective lenses (of ×2, ×5 and ×10).

    a State what ×2 on a lens means. **(1)**

....

....

    b The microscope has a ×7 eyepiece lens.
Calculate the possible total magnifications.
Show your working. **(3)**

....

....

....

....

2 When looking at plant root tissue under a microscope, Jenna notices that about 10 cells fit across the field of view.
She calculates the diameter of the field of view as 0.2 mm.
Estimate the diameter of one cell.
Show your working. **(2)**

....

....

....

....

....

....

3 Sasha draws a palisade cell from a star anise plant.
The cell has a length of 0.45 mm.

    a Sasha's drawing is magnified ×500.
Calculate the length of the cell in Sasha's drawing. **(1)**

....

....

....

    b Sasha adds a scale bar to show 0.1 mm.
Calculate the length of the scale bar. **(1)**

....

....

Amylase is an enzyme made in the salivary glands in your mouth and in the pancreas. It catalyses the breakdown of starch into smaller sugar molecules. The iodine test identifies the presence of starch, but does not react with sugar. You will use this test to show how effective amylase is in digesting starch at different pHs.

Your teacher may watch to see if you can:

- work safely
- collect accurate data.

Method

A Drop one drop of iodine solution into each depression of the dimple tile.

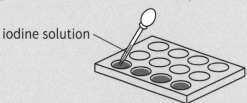

iodine solution

B Measure 2 cm³ of amylase solution into a test tube using a syringe.

C Add 1 cm³ of your pH solution to the test tube using a second syringe. Record the pH of the solution that you are using.

D Using a third syringe, add 2 cm³ starch solution to the mixture and start the stop clock. Use the pipette to stir the mixture.

E After 20 seconds, take a small amount of the mixture in the pipette and place one drop of it on the first iodine drop on the tile. Return the rest of the solution in the pipette to the test tube.

F If the iodine solution turns black, then there is still starch in the mixture and you should repeat step **E** (after 10 seconds). If it remains yellow, then all the starch is digested and you should record the time taken for this to happen.

G If there is time, repeat the experiment using a solution with a different pH.

Prediction

1 Predict at which pH the amylase will digest starch fastest. Explain your prediction. Record your prediction and explanation in the box below.

<table>
<tr><td>

</td></tr>
</table>

Aim

To investigate the effect of pH on the rate of digestion of starch by amylase.

Apparatus

- iodine solution in dropping bottle
- dimple tile
- test tubes
- test tube rack
- syringes
- pipette
- amylase solution
- starch solution
- solutions of specific pH
- stop clock

Safety ⚠

Eye protection should be worn.

Recording your results

2 Draw a table in the box below, to present these results clearly.

3 Collect data from all the groups in the class so that you have results for each of the different pHs. If you have more than one result for each pH, calculate a mean time for each one. Record the mean times in the box below.

Considering your results

4 Using the box below, plot a line graph to show the time taken for amylase to digest starch with the different pHs.

5 Look at your graph and use it to describe the effect of pH on the time taken for amylase to digest starch.

....

....

6 Suggest a reason for the shape of your graph.

....

....

Evaluation

7 Describe any problems you had with carrying out the experiment.

....

....

8 Suggest reasons for the problems and how the method could be changed to help reduce the problems.

....

....

....

9 Were any of the results surprising? If so, why?

....

....

10 Do you think you have enough results to support your conclusion? Explain your answer.

....

....

....

Use this section to record what you have learnt in this practical.
I can...

☐ describe the effect of pH on enzyme activity

☐ calculate the rate of enzyme activity from experimental data

☐ explain why pH affects enzyme activity.

Exam-style questions

1 Catalase is an enzyme that breaks down hydrogen peroxide into water and oxygen.
   Some students are investigating the effect of pH on this enzyme-controlled reaction by collecting
   the oxygen. One suggestion is to bubble the gas through water and collect it in an upturned
   measuring cylinder full of water. Another suggestion is to collect the water in a gas syringe.

   a Explain which method of gas collection you would use.   **(2)**

....

....

....

....

   b Explain how the students should measure the pH in their investigation.   **(2)**

....

....

....

....

   c The table shows the results from the students' investigation.
      Draw a graph to display the results.

Time (min)	Volume of O_2 released (cm^3)	
	at pH 3	at pH 6
1	1.4	1.6
2	2.7	3.2
3	4.2	5.6
4	5.9	5.7
5	6.6	8.4
6	8.4	10.6

(3)

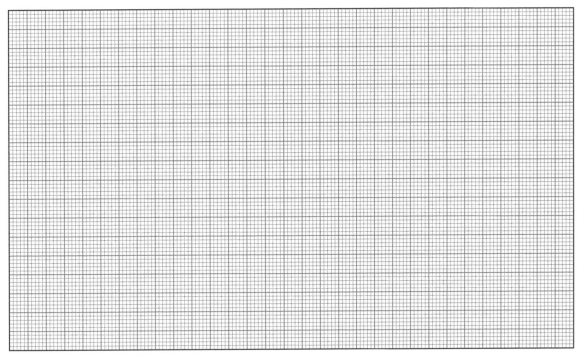

d Identify the anomalous result and suggest a reason for the error. **(2)**

....

....

....

e Calculate the average rate of reaction (average volume of oxygen produced per minute) at pH 6. **(1)**

....

....

....

2 Scientists working on bioleaching are interested in an enzyme called glucose oxidase, which is found in many microorganisms.

The graph shows the results from an investigation into the effect of pH on the rate of activity of glucose oxidase from two different types of bacteria.

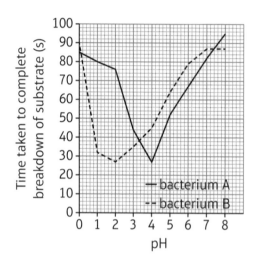

a What is the optimum pH for glucose oxidase from each type of bacterium? **(2)**

....

....

....

b Explain which enzyme is more active at pH 5. **(1)**

....

....

....

c Explain which bacterium might be more useful for bioleaching mine water. **(2)**

....

....

....

Osmosis is the overall movement of water molecules from a region where there are more of them in a particular volume to a region where there are fewer, through a semi-permeable membrane. The cells in a potato contain many substances dissolved in water. The cells are surrounded by cell membranes that are permeable to water. When a strip of potato is placed in a solution, the overall movement of water molecules between the potato cells and the solution will depend on which has the higher concentration of solutes. In this practical, you will investigate osmosis in potato strips in terms of the percentage change in mass of potato in different solutions.

Your teacher may watch to see if you can:

- measure accurately
- work carefully.

Method

A Using the waterproof pen, label each tube with the name of one of the solutions. Place the boiling tubes in the rack.

B Dry a potato strip carefully by blotting it with a paper towel. The potato strips can be removed using a cork borer, as shown in the diagram, or cut using a scalpel. This will have been done for you, before the experiment. Measure its mass on the balance.

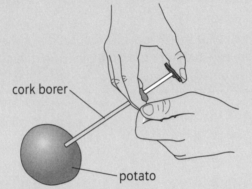

cork borer

potato

C Place the potato strip into one of the tubes. Record the label on the tube and the mass of the strip in your results table (see next page).

D Repeat steps **B** and **C** until all strips have been measured and placed in tubes.

E Carefully fill each tube with the appropriate solution, so that the potato is fully covered. Leave the tubes for at least 15 minutes.

F For each potato strip, use the forceps to remove it from its tube, blot dry on a paper towel and measure its mass again. Record all the masses in the results table.

Prediction

1 For each of the 4 solutions you will use, predict whether the potato strips will gain mass, lose mass or keep the same mass. Explain your predictions. Record your predictions and explanations in the box below.

Aim

To investigate how solution concentration affects percentage change in mass of potato strips due to osmosis.

Apparatus

- 4 potato strips
- accurate balance
- 4 boiling tubes and rack (or beakers)
- waterproof pen
- 4 sucrose solutions: 0%, 40%, 80%, 100%
- forceps
- paper towels

Safety

Do not drink any of the solutions or eat the potatoes.

....

....

....

....

....

....

Recording your results

2 Complete the first three columns of the table below, labelled 'Solution', 'A' and 'B', with the solution descriptions and your measurements from the experiment.

Solution	A Mass of potato strip at start (g)	B Mass of potato strip at end (g)	C Change in mass (g) = B – A	D % change in mass $= \dfrac{C}{A} \times 100\%$

3 Complete column **C** by calculating the change in mass for each potato strip using the formula shown.

4 Complete column **D** by calculating the percentage change in mass for each potato strip using the formula shown.

5 Compare the results for percentage change in mass from all groups in the class for each solution. Identify any results that seem very different from the others (outliers). Try to suggest a reason why they are so different.

....
....
....
....
....
....
....
....

6 Using all results except outliers, calculate a mean value for percentage change in mass for each solution.

7 Draw a suitable chart or graph to show the mean percentage change in the mass of each potato strip on the *y*-axis against the solution description on the *x*-axis.

Considering your results/conclusions

8 Describe the pattern shown in your chart or graph.

9 Explain the pattern shown in your chart or graph, using the word 'osmosis' in your answer.

10 Explain why you calculated percentage change in mass.

11 Explain why calculating a mean value from several repeats of the same experiment is more likely to give a value that can be reproduced by others.

Evaluation

12 Describe any problems that you had with the experiment. Suggest how these could be reduced or avoided to produce better results.

Use this section to record what you have learnt in this practical.
I can...
☐ calculate percentage gain and loss of mass in osmosis.

Exam-style questions

1   The table shows the results from an experiment similar to the one described in the method.

Tube	A	B	C	D
Sucrose concentration (g)	0	10	30	50
Mass of potato at start (g)	4.81	5.22	4.94	4.86
Mass of potato at end (g)	4.90	4.96	4.39	3.69

   a For each solution, calculate the gain or loss in mass of the potato piece. **(2)**

....

....

....

....

....

   b For each solution, calculate the percentage change in mass of the potato. **(2)**

....

....

....

....

....

   c Give a reason for the result from tube A. **(1)**

....

....

   d Explain the results for tubes B–D. **(2)**

....

....

....

....

   e Use the results to give the possible solute concentration of potato tissue, giving a reason
      for your answer. **(2)**

....

....

....

....

....

f Describe how the method could be adapted to give a more accurate answer to part **e**. **(1)**

....

....

....

....

....

....

2 The graph shows the results of an experiment comparing osmosis in tissue from a halophyte plant and a potato in the same solution.

a Identify, with a reason, which tissue lost water fastest over the first 5 minutes. **(2)**

....

....

....

....

b Explain why it lost water faster than the other tissue. **(2)**

....

....

....

....

c Calculate the average rate of change in mass over the first 4 minutes for the potato. **(1)**

....

....

....

....

Combined science   CC2d Core practical 1: Investigating inks

Ink is a mixture of coloured substances dissolved in a liquid solvent. In this practical, you will use simple distillation to separate a sample of the solvent in some ink.

Your teacher may watch to see if you can:

- carry out experiments safely, reducing the risks from hazards.

Method

A Set up your apparatus as shown in the diagram.

B Adjust the Bunsen burner so that you have a gentle blue flame. The air hole should be about half open and the gas tap should be about half on.

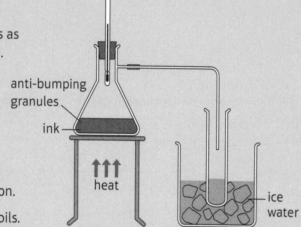

anti-bumping granules

ink

heat

ice water

C Heat the ink until it boils.

D Collect the distillate in the test tube and note the temperature of the vapour.

Planning and predicting

1 When you distil the ink, how will you know if you have successfully purified the water?

....
....
....

2 Predict the temperature reading on the thermometer when the ink is boiling. Explain your answer.

....
....

3 What is the purpose of the ice water shown in the diagram?

....
....

4 The conical flask might be knocked off the tripod.

   a Why is the conical flask a hazard if knocked over?

....
....

Aim

To use distillation to produce pure water from ink.

Apparatus

- eye protection
- conical flask with side arm
- delivery tube
- test tube
- ink
- Bunsen burner
- gauze
- rubber bung with thermometer
- 250 cm³ beaker
- ice
- tripod
- heat-resistant mat

Safety ⚠

Eye protection should be worn at all times.

Anti-bumping granules should be used to reduce the risk of the liquid boiling over.

b How can the risk of harm from this hazard be reduced?

5 Suggest one other hazard and a way of reducing the risk from this hazard.

6 What air hole and gas settings should you have for the Bunsen burner:

   a when you are not using it

   b when you are using it to heat the ink?

Considering your results

7 Did you purify the water successfully? Explain your answer.
Try to include a possible test you could carry out to prove it was water.

8 Explain what happened when the ink was distilled. In your explanation, use the following words:
boil, condenser, evaporate, liquid, steam, temperature, vapour.

Use this section to record what you have learnt in this practical.
I can...

- [ ] describe how to carry out and what happens in simple distillation
- [ ] explain what happens when distillation takes place
- [ ] explain what precautions are needed to reduce risk in a distillation experiment.

Exam-style questions

1   A student carries out simple distillation on a sample of blue ink.

   a Predict how the appearance of the ink changes, and give a reason for your answer.   **(2)**

....

....

....

....

   b During the experiment, hot liquid solvent drips from the bulb of the thermometer.
   Suggest an explanation for a temperature rise from 83 °C to 100 °C as this happens.   **(1)**

....

....

....

2   Explain why simple distillation allows a pure solvent to be separated from a solution.   **(3)**

....

....

....

....

....

3   A student distils a sample of ink.
   Devise a simple method to show that the liquid collected is pure water.
   Include the expected results in your answer.   **(3)**

....

....

....

....

....

....

....

....

Salts, such as copper sulfate, are compounds formed by reacting an acid with a base. Copper oxide reacts with warm sulfuric acid to produce a blue solution of the salt copper sulfate. In this practical, you will use these reactants to prepare pure, dry, hydrated copper sulfate crystals.

Your teacher may watch to see if you can:

- safely and correctly use apparatus.

Method

A Pour about 20 cm³ of dilute sulfuric acid into a conical flask.

B Place the conical flask into a water bath at 50 °C and heat for 3–4 minutes to allow the acid to heat up.

C Use the spatula to add a little copper oxide to the acid and stir or swirl the contents of the flask.

D Keep repeating step **C** until the black powder does not disappear after stirring. (This makes sure the copper oxide is in excess.)

E Return the mixture to the water bath for a few minutes (to make sure there is no acid left).

F Filter the mixture into a beaker and pour into an evaporating basin.

G Place the evaporating basin on top of a beaker half full of water. Heat the beaker, evaporating basin and contents using a Bunsen burner on a blue flame.

H Heat until about half of the water has evaporated. Then allow the evaporating basin to cool.

I When cool, transfer the solution to a Petri dish or watch glass and leave for a few days to allow the water to evaporate.

J Observe the shape and colour of the copper sulfate crystals formed.

Step F

Step H

Aim

To prepare a sample of pure, dry, hydrated copper sulfate crystals starting from copper oxide.

Apparatus

- eye protection
- 100 cm³ conical flask
- 100 cm³ beaker
- Bunsen burner
- gauze and tripod
- heat mat
- Petri dish or watch glass
- 100 cm³ measuring cylinder
- evaporating basin
- spatula
- stirring rod
- filter funnel
- filter paper
- tongs
- water bath (set at 50 °C)
- dilute sulfuric acid
- copper(II) oxide

Safety ⚠️

Wear eye protection at all times.

Recording your results

1 Describe the colour, shape and size of the copper sulfate crystals produced.

....

....

2 Describe the appearance of:

a the sulfuric acid

b the copper oxide

c the solution at the end of the reaction.

Considering your results

3 Write a word equation to show the reaction you have carried out.

4 State why you need to be sure excess copper oxide is added in step **D**.

5 What would happen in step **E** if there was still some acid left?

6 Name the substance left in the filter paper in step **F**.

7 What is dissolved in the solution that went through the filter paper?

8 Explain why this is an example of a neutralisation reaction.

9 What substance acts as a base in this reaction?

10 Write a symbol equation to show the reaction you have carried out. Include the state symbols. Use your answer to question 3 to help you.

Use this section to record what you have learnt in this practical.
I can...

☐ prepare pure, dry crystals of a metal salt

☐ explain why making a salt is an example of a neutralisation reaction

☐ write a symbol equation to represent a chemical reaction.

Exam-style questions

1 State why copper sulfate is described as a salt. **(1)**

....

2 In step **E**, explain why the copper oxide gets stuck in the filter paper while the
copper sulfate goes through it. **(2)**

....

....

3 Nickel chloride ($NiCl_2$) is a soluble salt.
It can be made by reacting insoluble nickel oxide (NiO) with hydrochloric acid (HCl).

a Write a word equation for this reaction. **(1)**

....

b Write a balanced equation with state symbols. **(2)**

....

c Briefly describe the three main stages involved in preparing a pure, solid sample of
nickel chloride. You can draw diagrams to help with your answer. **(3)**

....

....

....

....

....

....

4 Two class groups prepared some zinc chloride.
One group produced lots of very small crystals while the other group
produced larger crystals.
Suggest an explanation for the groups producing different-sized crystals. **(2)**

....

....

....

....

....

....

Stomach acid contains hydrochloric acid. Acid indigestion causes a burning feeling in the chest and throat. Antacids, which may contain magnesium hydroxide, are used to neutralise stomach acid to relieve indigestion. In this practical, you will use calcium hydroxide, which has similar properties to magnesium hydroxide, to investigate neutralisation.

Your teacher may watch to see if you can:

- carry out an experiment appropriately
- use apparatus accurately and safely.

Method

A Use the measuring cylinder to add 50 cm³ of dilute hydrochloric acid to the beaker.

B Estimate and record the pH of the contents of the beaker:

- Put a piece of universal indicator paper onto the white tile.
- Dip the end of the glass rod into the liquid, then tap it onto the universal indicator paper.
- Wait 30 seconds, then match the colour to the appropriate pH on the pH colour chart.
- Rinse the glass rod with water.

C Measure out 0.3 g of calcium hydroxide powder onto a piece of paper or a 'weighing boat'.

D Add the calcium hydroxide powder to the beaker, stir, then estimate and record the pH of the mixture.

E Repeat step **D** seven times so that you add a total of 2.4 g of calcium hydroxide powder to the acid.

Recording your results

1 In the space below, make a table to record the pH of the contents of the beaker. Use the columns for the mass of calcium hydroxide powder added, and the pH of the mixture. Remember to leave a row for the first pH measurement (before you have added any calcium hydroxide).

Aim

Powdered calcium hydroxide reacts with hydrochloric acid. Calcium chloride solution and water are produced:

$$Ca(OH)_2(s) + 2HCl(aq) \rightarrow CaCl_2(aq) + 2H_2O(l)$$

You will investigate what happens to the pH of a fixed volume of dilute hydrochloric acid when you add calcium hydroxide to it.

Apparatus

- eye protection
- 100 cm³ beaker
- 50 cm³ measuring cylinder
- ±0.1 g balance
- spatula
- stirring rod
- white tile
- universal indicator paper
- pH colour chart
- dilute hydrochloric acid
- calcium hydroxide powder
- graph paper

Safety ⚠

Wear eye protection. Calcium hydroxide is an irritant with a risk of serious damage to eyes. Dilute hydrochloric acid is an irritant.

Considering your results

2 Plot a line graph to show pH on the vertical axis and mass of calcium hydroxide added on the horizontal axis. Draw a curve of best fit.

3 Describe what happens to the pH of the reaction mixture as calcium hydroxide continues to be added.

....

....

....

4 Use your graph to determine the mass of calcium hydroxide that must be added to reach pH 7.

Evaluation

5 Explain one way to improve the accuracy of the experiment.

....

Use this section to record what you have learnt in this practical.

I can...

☐ carry out a neutralisation reaction

☐ use experimental data to construct a graph.

Exam-style questions

1 **a** Name the soluble salt formed when hydrochloric acid reacts with calcium hydroxide. **(1)**

....

b Write the balanced equation, including state symbols, for the reaction between calcium hydroxide powder and dilute hydrochloric acid. **(3)**

....

....

2 Give *two* reasons that explain why eye protection must be worn when using dilute hydrochloric acid. **(2)**

....

....

....

3 A student investigates the change in pH when calcium hydroxide powder is added to $100 \, cm^3$ of dilute hydrochloric acid.

a State *two* control variables in his experiment. **(2)**

....

....

b State the independent variable in his experiment. **(1)**

....

c Describe how the student could modify his experiment to investigate temperature changes instead of pH changes. **(1)**

....

....

....

4 The pH of a solution may be determined using universal indicator paper or using a pH meter.

a State why a pH meter must be calibrated using a solution with a known pH value. **(1)**

....

b Explain whether indicator paper or a pH meter has the higher resolution. **(2)**

....

....

....

In drag racing, the aim is to get to the end of a straight track as quickly as possible. The most important feature of the bike is its acceleration. Drag racers try to improve the performance of their bikes by changing the force produced by the engine and the tyres or by changing the mass of the bike. In this practical, you are going to use trolleys as a model of a motorbike to investigate the effects that mass and force have on acceleration.

Your teacher may watch to see if you can:

- follow instructions safely
- take careful measurements.

Method

A Prop up one end of the ramp and place a trolley on it. Adjust the slope of the ramp until the trolley just starts to move on its own. Gravity pulling the trolley down the slope is now slightly greater than the friction in the trolley's wheels.

B Stick a piece of card to the top of the trolley using sticky putty. Leave enough space to stack some masses on top of the trolley. Measure the length of the card and write it down.

C Find the mass of the trolley and write it down.

D Fasten the pulley at the bottom end of the ramp, and arrange the string and masses as shown below.

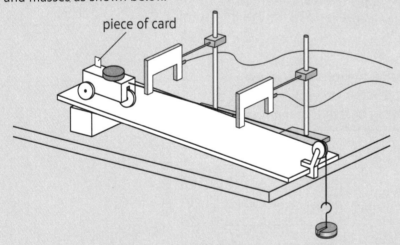

piece of card

Aim

To investigate the effect of mass on the acceleration of a trolley.

Apparatus

- trolley
- ramp
- blocks to prop up the end of the ramp
- string
- pulley
- masses
- sticky tape
- card
- sticky putty
- balance
- 2 light gates
- datalogger
- 2 clamps and stands
- box of crumpled newspaper

Safety

Make sure masses cannot fall on your feet by placing a box of crumpled newspaper on the floor beneath them.

E Set up two light gates, one near the top of the ramp and one near the bottom.
Adjust their positions so that the card on the top of the trolley passes through each gate as it runs down the ramp.

F Put a mass on the end of the string. You will keep this mass the same for all your tests. You will have to decide what mass to use.

G Release the trolley from the top of the ramp and write down the speed of the trolley (from the datalogger) as it passes through *each* light gate. Also write down the time it takes for the trolley to go from one light gate to the other.

H Repeat step **G** for other masses on the trolley. You will have to decide what masses to use, how many different masses you are going to test, and whether you need to repeat any of your tests.

Prediction

1 You will accelerate a trolley using a constant force. What effect do you think the mass of the trolley will have on the acceleration? Explain your prediction if you can. Record your prediction and ideas in the box below.

....

....

Recording your results

2 Record your results in the table below.

Mass added to trolley (kg)	Total mass of trolley and masses (kg)	Run number	u – 1st velocity reading (m/s)	v – 2nd velocity reading (m/s)	Time between velocity measurements (s)	Acceleration (m/s²)
		1				
		2				
		3				
		Mean				

3 Calculate the acceleration for each run using the formula in the box.

4 Find the mean acceleration for each trolley mass.

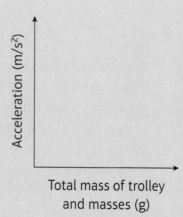

$$\text{acceleration} = \frac{\text{change in velocity}}{\text{time}}$$

$$a = \frac{(v - u)}{t}$$

Considering your results

5 Plot a scatter graph to show your results. Put the total mass of the trolley on the horizontal axis and the acceleration on the vertical axis, as shown in the diagram. Draw a line or curve of best fit through your points.

Acceleration (m/s²)

Total mass of trolley and masses (g)

6 a What relationship between acceleration and mass does your graph show?

b Is this what you predicted?

Evaluation

7 a How close are the points on your graph to the line of best fit?

b What does this tell you about the quality of the data you have gathered?

8 How do your results compare to the results obtained by other groups?

9 How certain are you that your conclusion is correct? Explain your answer.

Use this section to record what you have learnt in this practical.

I can...

- [ ] describe what acceleration is
- [ ] investigate the factors that affect the acceleration of an object.

Exam-style questions

1   The light gates and datalogger record the speed of the trolley at the top of the ramp and at the bottom of the ramp, and also record the time the trolley takes to move between the two light gates. Describe how this information can be used to calculate the acceleration.   **(2)**

....

....

....

....

2   Use the results shown in this graph to draw a conclusion for this part of the investigation.   **(1)**

Force pulling on trolley (N)

....

....

....

....

....

....

3   Look at this graph.

Total mass of trolley and the masses on it (kg)

   a Use this graph to draw a conclusion for this part of the investigation.   **(1)**

....

....

   b Explain how you would present the data in this graph to allow you to draw a better conclusion.   **(2)**

....

....

....

The speed, frequency and wavelength of waves can be measured in different ways. The most suitable equipment for carrying out these measurements depends on the type of wave and on its speed.

Your teacher may watch to see if you can:

- follow instructions carefully
- make accurate measurements.

Part 1. Speed of waves on water

Method

A Set up a ripple tank with a straight dipper near one of the short sides of the tank. Fasten a ruler to one of the long sides so you can see the markings above the water level.

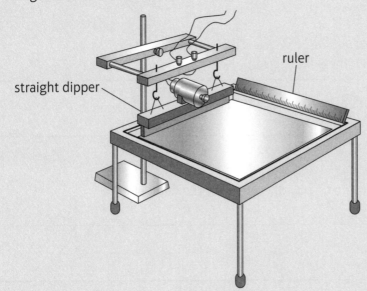

straight dipper

ruler

B Vary the current to the motor until you get waves with a wavelength about half as long as the ripple tank (so you can always see two waves).

C Count how many waves are formed in 10 seconds and write it down in the space below.

D Look at the waves against the ruler. Use the markings on the ruler to estimate the wavelength of the waves. If you have one, use a camera to take a photo of the waves with a ruler held just above them. Write your estimated wavelength down in the space below.

E Mark two points on the edge of the ripple tank and measure the distance between them. Use the stopwatch to find out how long it takes a wave to go from one mark to the other. Add this value to your other pieces of data below.

Recording your results

Number of waves counted [Step **C**]:

Estimated wavelength [Step **D**]:

Distance between two points [Step **E**]:

Time taken for wave to go between two points [Step **E**]:

Aim

To measure waves in different ways and evaluate the suitability of the equipment.

Apparatus

- ripple tank
- stopwatch
- ruler
- digital camera

Safety ⚠

Mop up any spilled water straight away.

Using your results

1   Calculate the speed of a single wave by dividing the distance by the time (both from step **E**). Make sure your distance is in metres and your time is in seconds.

2   Find the frequency by taking the number of waves in 10 seconds (from step **C**) and dividing by 10. Then calculate the speed of the series of waves by multiplying the wavelength (from step **D**) by the frequency you have just worked out.

Considering your results/conclusions

3   Compare your results from questions **1** and **2** with results obtained by other groups. Are your results similar? If not, can you explain the differences?

Evaluation

4   How easy was it to measure the frequency in step **C**? Why did you count the number of waves in 10 seconds?

5   How easy was it to measure the wavelength in step **D**? It was suggested that you use a camera to help you do this. What benefit would there be in doing this?

6   How easy was it to time a single wave in step **E**? Is there any way you could improve this measurement?

Use this section to record what you have learnt in this practical.
I can...
☐ investigate waves a in liquid
☐ calculate speed and frequency of a wave
☐ evaluate my experiment and suggest improvements.

Part 2. Measuring waves in a solid

Method

A   Suspend a metal rod horizontally using clamp stands and rubber bands, as shown in the diagram below.

B   Hit one end of the rod with a hammer. Hold a smartphone with a frequency app near the rod and note down the peak frequency.

C   Measure the length of the rod and write it down. The wavelength will be twice the length of the rod.

Apparatus

- metre rule
- hammer
- 2 clamps and stands
- long metal rod
- rubber bands
- smartphone with frequency app

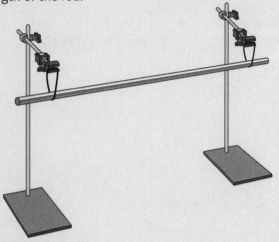

Recording your results

1   Use the frequency (from step **B**) and the wavelength (from step **C**) to calculate the speed of sound in the metal rod.

Frequency [step **B**]:

Wavelength [step **C**]:

Your calculation for the speed of sound in the metal rod:

Considering your results/conclusions

2   What is the speed of sound in the material you tested?

....

....

Evaluation

3   Explain which of your measurements is the more accurate: the wavelength or the frequency.

....

....

4   Complete the table to summarise the equipment you used for the measurements in both parts of this investigation, and how suitable the equipment was.

What was measured?	Which material was this measured for?	How was it measured?	Why was this method chosen?

5   You can measure walking speed using a tape measure and a stopwatch. Explain why these instruments are not suitable for measuring the speed of sound in a solid.

....

....

....

....

Use this section to record what you have learnt in this practical.
I can...

☐ investigate waves in a solid

☐ calculate speed

☐ evaluate the suitability of the equipment used.

Exam-style questions

1 A sound wave in air travels 660 metres in 2 seconds.
Calculate the speed of the sound wave. **(2)**

....

....

....

....

....

2 A sound wave travelling in water has a frequency of 100 Hz.
The speed of sound in water is 1482 m/s.
Calculate the wavelength of the wave. **(2)**

....

....

....

....

....

3 Adanna is watching waves on the sea go past two buoys.
She knows the buoys are 20 metres apart.
Describe how she can find the speed of the waves. **(2)**

....

....

....

....

....

4 The speed of sound in air can be measured by finding the time it takes for a sound to echo
from a nearby wall, and measuring the distance to the wall.

Hitting the end of a metal rod with a hammer causes sound waves to travel along the rod.
They reflect from the far end of the rod and continue to move up and down the rod until
the energy dissipates. Give a reason why the method used for finding the speed of sound
in air cannot be used for finding the speed of sound in a metal. **(2)**

....

....

....

....

Electromagnetic waves travel at different speeds in different materials. Light slows down when it goes from air into glass or water. If light hits the interface at an angle, it changes direction. This is called refraction. In this practical, you will investigate how the direction of a ray of light changes as it enters and leaves a glass block.

Aim

To investigate how light is affected when it travels from air into glass, or from glass into air.

Your teacher may watch to see if you can:

- measure angles accurately.

Apparatus

- ray box with single slit
- power supply
- rectangular glass block
- ruler
- protractor
- plain paper

Method

A   Place a piece of plain paper on the desk. Set up the power supply, ray box and single slit so that you can shine a single ray of light across the paper on your desk.

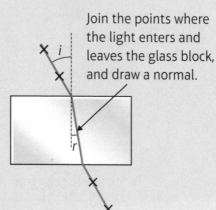

Join the points where the light enters and leaves the glass block, and draw a normal.

Safety ⚠

Ray boxes may get hot.

B   Place a rectangular glass block on the paper. Draw around the block.

C   Shine a ray of light into your block. Use small crosses to mark where the rays of light go.

D   Take the block off the paper. Use a ruler to join the crosses and show the path of the light, and extend the line so it meets the outline of the block. Join the points where the light entered and left the block to show where it travelled inside the block.

E   Measure the angles of incidence and refraction where the light entered the block, and measure the angles where it left the block.

F   Repeat steps **C** to **E** with the ray entering the block at different angles.

G   Move the ray box so that the light ray reaches the interface at right angles. Note what happens to the light as it enters and leaves the block.

Recording your results

1   Record your results in this table.

Air to glass (light entering the block)		Glass to air (light leaving the block)	
Angle *i*	Angle *r*	Angle *i*	Angle *r*

2 Draw a scatter graph to show your results. Put the angle of incidence on the horizontal axis. Plot the air-to-glass points and draw a smooth curve of best fit. Repeat for the glass-to-air points, on the same set of axes.

Considering your results

3 Describe the results shown by your graph.

....

....

4 How does the direction of the ray of light leaving the glass block compare with that of the ray entering it?

....

....

5 Write a conclusion for your investigation.

....

....

Evaluation

6 a How accurate were your measurements?

b Is there any way you could improve your measurements?

....

....

Exam-style questions

1 Describe the difference between the way that light travels through glass compared with the way in which it travels through air. **(1)**

....

....

2 The table shows a student's results from this investigation.

Air to glass		Glass to air	
i	r	i	r
10°	6°	6°	6°
20°	13°	13°	20°
30°	20°	20°	31°
40°	25°	25°	40°
50°	30°	30°	50°
60°	34°	34°	58°
70°	38°	38°	69°
80°	40°	40°	78°

a Use the data in the table to plot a scatter graph to show the results for light going from air to glass. Put the angle of incidence on the horizontal axis, and join your points with a smooth curve of best fit. **(5)**

b Use the table and your graph to write a conclusion for this part of the investigation. **(3)**

....

....

....

....

....

....

....

c Use your graph to find the angle of refraction when the angle of incidence is 15°. **(1)**

....

....

....

....

3 If light passes through a glass block with parallel sides, the ray that comes out should be parallel with the ray that goes in. This means that the angle of incidence for air to glass should be the same as the angle of refraction from glass to air.

Look at the table in question **2**. Suggest one source of random error that may have caused the differences in these angles. **(1)**

....

....

....

....

Equations in the left hand column are ones you may be asked to *recall and apply* in your exam.

You do not need to recall the equations in the right hand column, but you should be able to select and apply them in an exam.

Equations for Higher tier only are marked with the Higher icon.

Recall and apply	Select and apply
Unit SP1 Motion	
distance travelled = average speed × time $$d = x \times t$$ acceleration = change in velocity ÷ time taken $$a = \frac{(v - u)}{t}$$	(final velocity)² − (initial velocity)² = 2 × acceleration × distance $$v^2 - u^2 = 2 \times a \times s$$
Unit SP2 Motion and Forces	
force = mass × acceleration $$F = m \times a$$ weight = mass × gravitational field strength $$W = m \times g$$ **H** momentum = mass × velocity $$p = m \times v$$ work done = force × distance moved in the direction of the force $$E = F \times d$$ kinetic energy = $\frac{1}{2}$ × mass × (speed)² $$KE = \frac{1}{2} \times m \times v^2$$	**H** force = change in momentum ÷ time $$F = \frac{(mv - mu)}{t}$$
Unit SP3 Conservation of Energy	
change in gravitational potential energy = mass × gravitational field strength × change in vertical height $$GPE = m \times g \times h$$ efficiency = $\dfrac{\text{useful energy transferred by the device}}{\text{total energy supplied to the device}}$	
Unit SP4 Waves	
wave speed = frequency × wavelength $$v = f \times \lambda$$ wave speed = distance ÷ time $$v = \frac{x}{t}$$	
Unit SP8 Energy – Forces Doing Work	
power = work done ÷ time taken $$P = \frac{E}{t}$$	
Unit SP9 Forces and their Effects	
moment of a force = force × distance normal to the direction of the force	

Recall and apply	Select and apply

Unit SP10 Electricity and circuits

charge = current × time

$$Q = I \times t$$

energy transferred = charge moved × potential difference

$$E = Q \times V$$

potential difference = current × resistance

$$V = I \times R$$

power = energy transferred ÷ time taken

$$P = \frac{E}{t}$$

electrical power = current × potential difference

$$P = I \times V$$

electrical power = current squared × resistance

$$P = I^2 \times R$$

Select and apply:

energy transferred = current × potential difference × time

$$E = I \times V \times t$$

Unit SP12 Magnetism and the Motor Effect

H force on a conductor at right angles to a magnetic field carrying a current = magnetic flux density × current × length

$$F = B \times I \times l$$

Unit SP13 Electromagnetic Induction

H $\dfrac{\text{potential difference across primary coil}}{\text{potential difference across secondary coil}} = \dfrac{\text{number of turns in primary coil}}{\text{number of turns in secondary coil}}$

$$\frac{V_p}{V_s} = \frac{N_p}{N_s}$$

For transformers with 100% efficiency,

potential difference across primary coil × current in primary coil = potential difference across secondary coil × current in secondary coil

$$V_p \times I_p = V_s \times I_s$$

Unit SP14 Particle Model

density = mass ÷ volume

$$\rho = \frac{m}{V}$$

Select and apply:

change in thermal energy = mass × specific heat capacity × change in temperature

$$\Delta Q = m \times c \times \Delta \theta$$

thermal energy for a change of state = mass × specific latent heat

$$Q = M \times L$$

to calculate pressure or volume for gases of fixed mass at constant temperature

$$P_1 \times V_1 = P_2 \times V_2$$

Unit SP15 Forces and Matter

force exerted on a spring = spring constant × extension

$$F = k \times x$$

pressure = force normal to surface ÷ area of surface

$$P = \frac{F}{A}$$

Select and apply:

energy transferred in stretching = 0.5 × spring constant × (extension)²

$$E = \frac{1}{2} \times k \times x^2$$

H pressure due to a column of liquid = height of column × density of liquid × gravitational field strength

$$P = h \times \rho \times g$$

CB1b

Exam-style questions

1 a the lens makes things appear two times bigger (1)
   b $2 \times 7 = \times 14$, $5 \times 7 = \times 35$, $10 \times 7 = \times 70$ (3)

2 diameter of 10 cells is 0.2 mm, so diameter of one cell = 0.2/10 = 0.02 mm (2: 1 for working, 1 for correct answer with units)

3 a $0.45 \times 500 = 225$ mm (or 22.5 cm) (1)
   b $0.1 \times 500 = 50$ mm (or 5 cm) (1)

CB1g

Exam-style questions

1 a gas syringe (1) with any suitable reason, such as some of the oxygen might dissolve in water (if the upturned measuring cylinder was used), or the scale on the syringe might be finer so giving more accurate readings. (1)
   b use a pH meter (1) because:
      • universal/pH indicator solution might interfere with the reaction
      • OR a pH meter is more accurate
      • OR universal/pH indicator is not accurate/sensitive enough to distinguish between small pH increments
   c Graph drawn from data in table:
      • axes drawn with suitable scales and labelled appropriately (1)
      • points plotted accurately and joined by one curved line for each pH (1)
      • both lines drawn on same axes (1)
   d Measurement taken at 4 mins for pH 6 is too low compared to the rest of the results (1). Any suitable reason that explains the low result, such as scale was not read accurately (1).
   e 10.6 cm³ produced in 6 mins = $\frac{10.6}{6}$ = 1.77 cm³/min

2 a bacterium A: pH 4 (1); bacterium B: pH 2 (1)
   b The enzyme from bacterium A (1) because it takes less time to break down the substrate than the enzyme from bacterium B (1).
   c Bacterium A (1) because its optimum pH is the most acidic (1).

CB1h

Exam-style questions

1 a 0% + 0.09 g; 10% – 0.26 g; 30% – 0.55 g; 50% – 1.17 g (1 mark for correct values, 1 mark for units and correctly identifying gain or loss)
   b 0% + 1.9%; 10% – 5.0%; 30% – 11.1%; 50% – 24.1% (1 mark for correct values, 1 mark for units and correctly identifying gain or loss)
   c The slice gained mass because osmosis took place into the root from the surrounding water (1).
   d All the slices lost mass, but the percentage loss in mass increases as the solution concentration increases (1). This is because osmosis happens faster as the difference in concentration between the potato tissue and solution increases (1).
   e A concentration equivalent to between 0% and 10% sucrose solution (1), because when the concentrations are equal there will be no change in mass (1).
   f Any suitable suggestion that identifies how accuracy can be increased, such as using a range of solutions between 0% and 10% (1).

2 a The potato lost water fastest (1), because the gradient of its line is steeper than for the halophyte (1).
   b Potato has a lower solute concentration inside its cells than the halophyte (1), so will lose water faster by osmosis than the halophyte when placed in a concentrated solution (1).
   c Rate of change = $\frac{-8.2}{6}$ = –1.4% per minute (1)

CC2d

1 The liquid you have produced (the distillate) will be clear and colourless, the ink colour should not appear in the distillate.

2 The answer should be around 100 °C as this is the boiling point of water; however, values slightly below 100 °C are acceptable providing the reason given links to impurities.

3 to keep the test tube cool (and condense the vapour back into a liquid)

4 a The glass might smash and therefore there are risk of cuts; boiling water could spill and risk of this going onto clothes and skin; people could slip due to spilt water on the floor.
   b Stand up while doing practical work; so that you can more easily move out of the way; along with making sure that the tripod is stable and that the flask is steady; use a clamp and stand to secure the flask in place.

5 Any suitable hazard; together with one way of reducing the risk – e.g. hazard from liquid boiling over; reducing the risk could include the use of anti-bumping granules.

6 a air hole closed (yellow flame); makes the flame more visible (luminous); so reducing the risk of someone touching the flame accidentally
   b air hole slightly/half open; gas tap turned about half on; makes sure heating is gentle; helping to reduce the risk of the liquid boiling over and avoids depositing soot onto the gauze/flask

7 Your answer should refer to your actual results and how well this compared to the success criteria you set out in Q1 above. Possible tests for water could be: adding the distillate to anhydrous copper sulfate which turns blue (with water) or using cobalt chloride paper which turns purple/pink (with water).

8 Your answer should include:
   • ink/liquid is heated until it boils
   • liquid/water evaporates and turns into steam, also known as water vapour
   • steam is pure water vapour, so the temperature reading on the thermometer is 100 °C
   • the steam/vapour passes into the condenser, where it cools down
   • when it cools it turns from a vapour/gas back into a liquid
   • the pure water collects as the distillate

Exam-style questions

1 a It becomes darker (1) because it becomes more concentrated / solvent leaves the ink but the coloured substances do not (1).
   b The solvent was not pure / it was a mixture of liquids (1).

2 Solvent has a lower boiling point than the solute / solvent is liquid, but solute is solid at room temperature (1); solvent boils and leaves the solution (1); solvent vapour is cooled and condensed away from the solution (1).

3 Heat the liquid until it boils (1); measure its boiling point (1); pure water boils at 100 °C (1).

CC8c

1 The crystals are blue and diamond shaped. (The size will vary depending on conditions.)

2 a clear solution
   b black solid (powder)
   c blue solution

3 copper oxide + sulfuric acid → copper sulfate + water

4 so that all the acid is used up

5 The acid would react with the excess copper oxide and some or all of it would disappear.

6 copper oxide

7 copper sulfate

8 because the hydrogen ions of the acid are removed (and a salt and water are formed)

9 copper oxide

10 $CuO(s) + H_2SO_4(aq) \rightarrow CuSO_4(aq) + H_2O(l)$

Exam-style questions

1 because it is formed by the reaction between a base and an acid (1)

2 The copper oxide is a solid (made up of larger particles) that gets stuck in the filter paper (1). The particles of the copper sulfate are in solution (smaller) so pass through the filter paper (1).

3 a nickel oxide + hydrochloric acid → nickel chloride + water (1)

 b $NiO(s) + 2HCl(aq)$ (1) → $NiCl_2(aq) + H_2O(l)$ (1)

 c Step 1: add excess nickel oxide to some (dilute) hydrochloric acid (1).
 Step 2: filter out excess nickel oxide (1).
 Step 3: evaporate water to leave nickel chloride (1).

4 Small crystals are produced by fast evaporation of the water in the solution (1). Large crystals are produced by slow evaporation of the water in the solution (1).

CC8d

Suitable table drawn: two columns; first column labelled mass of $Ca(OH)_2$ power added/(g); second column labelled pH of the mixture; sufficient rows for nine readings.

Graph plotted with pH on vertical axis, mass of $Ca(OH)_2$ added (g) on horizontal axis; curve of best fit drawn; suitable title included.

Expected results: pH increases as more calcium hydroxide is added; end-point is 1.85 g; solubility of $Ca(OH)_2$ is about 0.17 g per 100 cm³ H_2O; so beyond this excess $Ca(OH)_2$ is seen.

Intercept at pH 7 identified; mass read from graph.

Improvement suggested, e.g. use more precuse balance (±0.01 g or ±0.001 g); increase volume of acid used; use narrow range indicator paper; use pH meter.

Exam-style questions

1 a calcium chloride (1)

 b $Ca(OH)_2(aq) + 2HCl(aq)$ → $CaCl_2(aq) + 2H_2O(l)$ 1 mark for formulae, 1 mark for balancing, 1 mark for state symbols

2 to avoid damage to eyes (1) because hydrochloric acid is irritant/corrosive (1)

3 a volume of acid (1); concentration of acid (1)

 b pH of reaction mixture (1)

 c use a thermometer instead of indicator paper or a pH meter (1)

4 a to make sure that it gives an accurate pH value / pH value close to the true value (1)

 b the pH meter has the higher resolution because it gives readings to 1 or 2 decimal places (1) but universal indicator paper only gives readings to the nearest whole pH unit (1)

CP2d

6 a Acceleration decreases as mass increases. (Acceleration is inversely proportional to mass, although students cannot determine that the relationship *is* one of inverse proportion without plotting a graph of acceleration against 1/mass and obtaining a straight line.)

Exam-style questions

1 Acceleration is a change in speed over time (1), so find the difference in the two speeds and divide by the time taken to move between the two light gates (1).

2 The acceleration is proportional to the force (1).

3 a The acceleration gets less as the mass increases (1). *Do not accept 'the acceleration is inversely proportional to the mass' at this point, as this cannot be determined for certain from the shape of the graph.*

 b Plot acceleration against 1/mass (or mass against 1/acceleration) (1); if this is a straight line it will show that the acceleration is inversely proportional to the accelerating mass (1).

CP4b.1

1 Students' own results.

2 Students' own results.

3 Results may vary because of different water depths (and different frequencies/wavelengths for the measurement of the series of waves).

4 There may be less than one wave in a second/any errors in counting the waves are spread out over 10 s, so this will give a more accurate value.

5 Comments are likely to mention the difficulty of measuring the wavelength while the waves were moving. The camera 'freezes' the motion of the waves so it is easier to take a precise and accurate measurement.

6 Comments are likely to relate to the speed of the wave; difficult to measure an accurate time when something is moving fast. Suggestions could include using a video camera with a time also displayed.

CP4b.2

1 Students' own results.

2 Students' own results.

3 Students could justify either answer: the wavelength, as this is obtained from a static measurement of the rod; the frequency, as this is measured electronically.

4 Students' own table.

5 The sound travels too fast to use a stopwatch/human reaction time would introduce errors greater than the time being measured.

Exam-style questions

1 speed = $\dfrac{660\,m}{2\,s}$ = 330 m/s (1 for substitution, 1 for evaluation)

2 wavelength = $\dfrac{1482\,m}{s/100\,Hz}$ = 148.2 m (1 for substitution, 1 for evaluation)

3 Use a stopwatch to find how long it takes one wave to go from one buoy to the other (1), and calculate the speed by dividing 20 m by the measured time (1).

4 The speed of sound in a metal is much higher than in air (1), and the time between a sound being made and its echo reaching the end of a rod is too short to be measured using a stopwatch (1).

CP5a
Exam-style questions

1 light travels more slowly / at a different speed in glass (1)

2 a Graph with sensible scales on axes (1) and axes labelled (1) All points correctly plotted to ± half a square (2) *Only 1 mark if one point plotted in error, 0 marks if more than one error.* Smooth curve passing through all the points (1).

 b The angle of refraction increases as the angle of incidence increases (1), but the angle of refraction is always less than the angle of incidence (1). The relationship between the angles of incidence and refraction is not a linear/proportional relationship (1).

 c the answer should be 9.5° (from the values supplied for plotting the graph), accept ± 1° (1)

3 The student may not have measured the angles accurately / may not have drawn the normal correctly (1).

Combined science

Practical skills sheet

These are the skills that you could have practised in each of the practicals. Use a highlighter pen to highlight each technique when you have covered them in your practical work. The skills that have not been covered in this book are covered in Lab Book 2.

Biology

Practical skill covered	Core practical	CB1b	CB1g	CB1h
B1 Use of appropriate apparatus to make a record a range of measurements accurately, including length, area, mass, time, temperature, volume of liquids and gases, and pH		✓	✓	✓
B2 Safe use of appropriate heating devices and techniques, including use of a Bunsen burner and a water bath or electric heater				
B3 Use of appropriate apparatus and techniques for the observation and measurement of biological changes and/or processes		✓	✓	✓
B4 Safe and ethical use of living organisms (plants or animals) to measure physiological functions and responses to the environment				
B5 Measurement of rates of reaction by a variety of methods including production of gas, uptake of water and colour change of indicator			✓	✓
B6 Applications of appropriate sampling techniques to investigate the distribution and abundance of organisms in an ecosystem via direct use in the field				
B7 Use of appropriate apparatus, techniques and magnification, including microscopes, to make observations of biological specimens and produce labelled scientific drawings		✓		

Chemistry

Practical skill covered	Core practical	CC2d	CC8c	CC8d
C1 Use of appropriate apparatus to make a record a range of measurements accurately, including mass, time, temperature, and volume of liquids and gases		✓	✓	✓
C2 Safe use of appropriate heating devices and techniques, including use of a Bunsen burner and a water bath or electric heater		✓	✓	
C3 Use of appropriate apparatus and techniques for conducting and monitoring chemical reactions, including appropriate reagents and/or techniques for the measurement of pH in different situations				✓
C4 Safe use of a range of equipment to purify and/or separate chemical mixtures, including evaporation, filtration, crystallisation, chromatography and distillation		✓	✓	
C5 Making and recording of appropriate observations during chemical reactions including changes in temperature and the measurement of rates of reaction by a variety of methods such as production of gas and colour change				✓
C6 Safe use and careful handling of gases, liquids and solids, including careful mixing of reagents under controlled conditions, using appropriate apparatus to explore chemical changes and/or products		✓	✓	✓
C7 Use of appropriate apparatus and techniques to draw, set up and use electrochemical cells for separation and production of elements and compounds				

Physics

Practical skill covered	Core practical	CP2d	CP4b	CP5a
P1 Use of appropriate apparatus to make a record a range of measurements accurately, including length, area, mass, time, volume and temperature. Use of such measurements to determine densities of solid or liquid objects		✓	✓	
P2 Use of appropriate apparatus to measure and observe the effects of forces including the extension of springs		✓		
P3 Use of appropriate apparatus and techniques for measuring motion, including determination of speed and rate of change of speed (acceleration/deceleration)		✓		
P4 Making observations of waves in fluids and solids to identify the suitability of apparatus to measure speed/frequency/wavelength. Making observations of the effects of the interaction of the electromagnetic waves with matter			✓	✓
P5 Safe use of appropriate apparatus in a range of contexts to measure energy changes/transfers and associated values such as work done				
P6 Use of appropriate apparatus to measure current, potential difference (voltage) and resistance, and to explore the characteristics of a variety of circuit elements				
P7 Use of circuit diagrams to construct and check series and parallel circuits including a variety of common circuit elements				